MORE FUN WITH MATHS

Compiled by John Drinkwater
Illustrated by David Mostyn

Ladybird Books

Number patterns

Using the number grid below, count in **5s** from 0.
Colour the **top left** corner of every fifth square **blue**.

Now count in **10s** from 0. Colour the **top right** corner of every tenth square **red**.

Count in **4s** and colour the **bottom left** corner of every fourth square **yellow**.

Finally, count in **3s** and colour the **bottom right** corner of every third square **green**.

CAN YOU SEE THE PATTERNS?
I'VE DONE A FEW FOR YOU.

IT'S EASY!

0	1	2	3	4	5	6	7	8	9
10	11	12	13	14	15	16	17	18	19
20	21	22	23	24	25	26	27	28	29
30	31	32	33	34	35	36	37	38	39
40	41	42	43	44	45	46	47	48	49
50	51	52	53	54	55	56	57	58	59
60	61	62	63	64	65	66	67	68	69
70	71	72	73	74	75	76	77	78	79
80	81	82	83	84	85	86	87	88	89
90	91	92	93	94	95	96	97	98	99

Which number apart from 0 has four coloured squares?

Counting in 5s and 10s

Can you count in 5s? Fill in the boxes.

5 → 10 → ☐ → ☐ → ☐ → ☐ → 35

Carry on counting in 5s.

40 → ☐ → ☐ → ☐ → ☐ → 65 → ☐

Now count in 10s.

10 → 20 → ☐ → ☐ → 50 → ☐ → ☐

Count in 10s starting from 7.

7 → 17 → ☐ → ☐ → ☐ → ☐ → ☐

Dot to dot

Join the dots to complete the picture.
You must join only the multiples of **10**.

0 → 10 → 20 → 30 and so on.

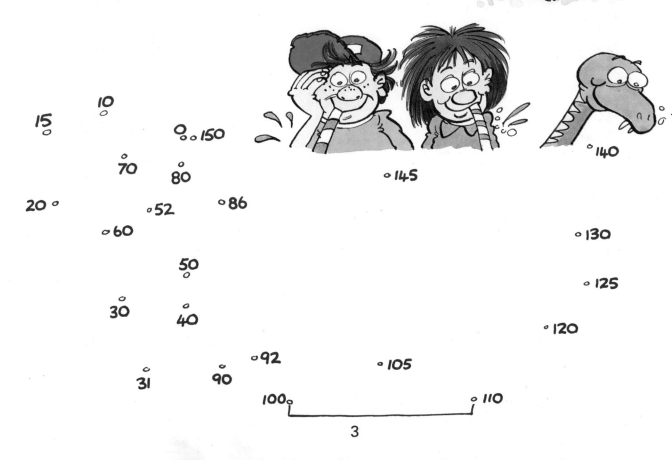

3

Repeated addition (multiplying)

Group these rabbits into sets of two.

How many sets are there? ☐

How many rabbits altogether? ☐

We can work this out by doing a long sum:
2 + 2 + 2 + 2 + 2 = 10

A quicker way of writing this would be:
5 sets of 2 equals 10 or **5(2) → 10**

Write these long sums the quick way, then fill in the answers.

2 + 2 + 2 + 2 + 2 + 2 + 2 = ☐7(2)☐ → ☐14☐

5 + 5 + 5 + 5 = ☐ → ☐

6 + 6 + 6 = ☐ → ☐

1 + 1 + 1 + 1 + 1 + 1 + 1 + 1 + 1 = ☐ → ☐

4 + 4 + 4 + 4 + 4 + 4 + 4 = ☐ → ☐

3 + 3 + 3 + 3 + 3 = ☐ → ☐

0 + 0 + 0 + 0 + 0 + 0 + 0 = ☐ → ☐

7 + 7 + 7 = ☐ → ☐

9 + 9 = ☐ → ☐

> USE THE NUMBER LINE AT THE BOTTOM OF THE PAGE. I'VE DONE THE FIRST TWO!

Now try these.

2(7) → ☐14☐   4(2) → ☐   2(9) → ☐

3(5) → ☐   2(0) → ☐   4(6) → ☐

1 2 3 4 5 6 7 8 9 10 11 12 13 14 15 16 17

4

Multiplication

Here are five dogs.
Each dog has four legs.
How many legs altogether?

$4 + 4 + 4 + 4 + 4 = 5(4) \rightarrow 20$

This can also be written like this: **5 × 4 = 20**

This is a **multiplication** sum.

Complete the table below.

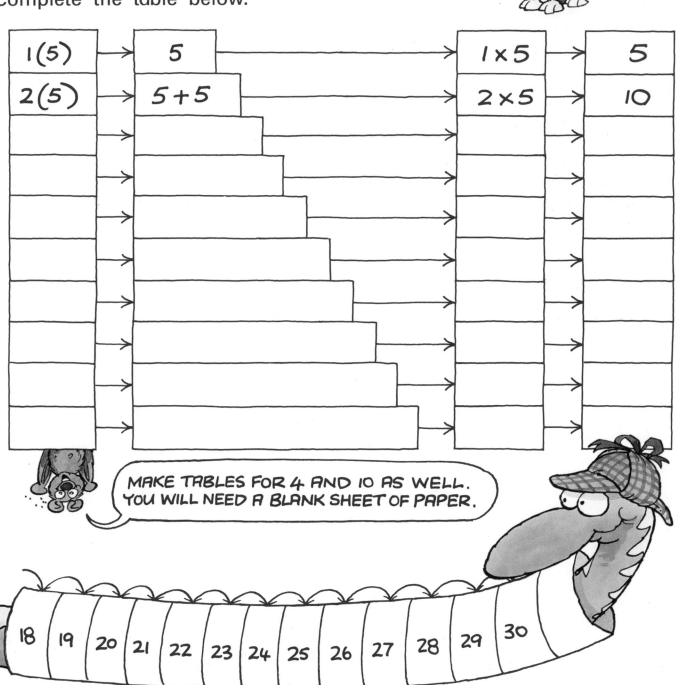

| 1(5) | → | 5 | → | 1 × 5 | → | 5 |
| 2(5) | → | 5 + 5 | → | 2 × 5 | → | 10 |

MAKE TABLES FOR 4 AND 10 AS WELL.
YOU WILL NEED A BLANK SHEET OF PAPER.

18 19 20 21 22 23 24 25 26 27 28 29 30

Numbers to the nearest ten

Here you can see some spiders.
There are three sets of ten and four ones, or units.

There are **34** spiders altogether.
You could also say there are **30 spiders to the nearest ten.**

Numbers ending in 5, 6, 7, 8 or 9 units are rounded **up** to the nearest ten.

For example:

> IN TENS AND UNITS, THE TENS ARE ALWAYS WRITTEN FIRST – 3 TENS – AND 4 UNITS.

three tens and seven units	→	37 altogether	→	40 to the nearest ten

five tens and two units		altogether		to the nearest ten
four tens and six units		altogether		to the nearest ten
seven tens and seven units		altogether		to the nearest ten
six tens and two units		altogether		to the nearest ten
eight tens and five units		altogether		to the nearest ten
four tens and nine units		altogether		to the nearest ten

MEET THE BOYS!

I LIKE SUMS I DO!

The highest number is ☐

Ordering numbers

Here are some numbers between 0 and 100.
Sort them into order starting with the highest number.

100   50   0   20   70   90   10   40

☐ ☐ ☐ ☐ ☐ ☐ ☐ ☐

HIGHEST

This monster has swallowed a lot of numbers.

He swallowed them in order starting with the lowest.
Sort the numbers into the same order that he swallowed them.

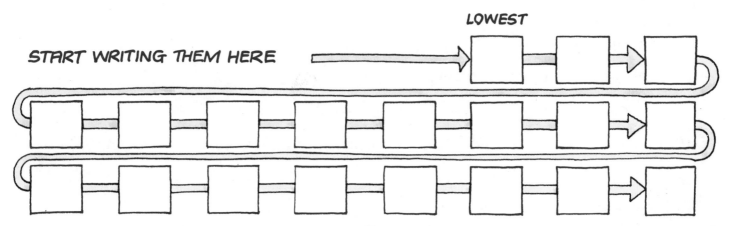

7

Clockwise or anticlockwise?

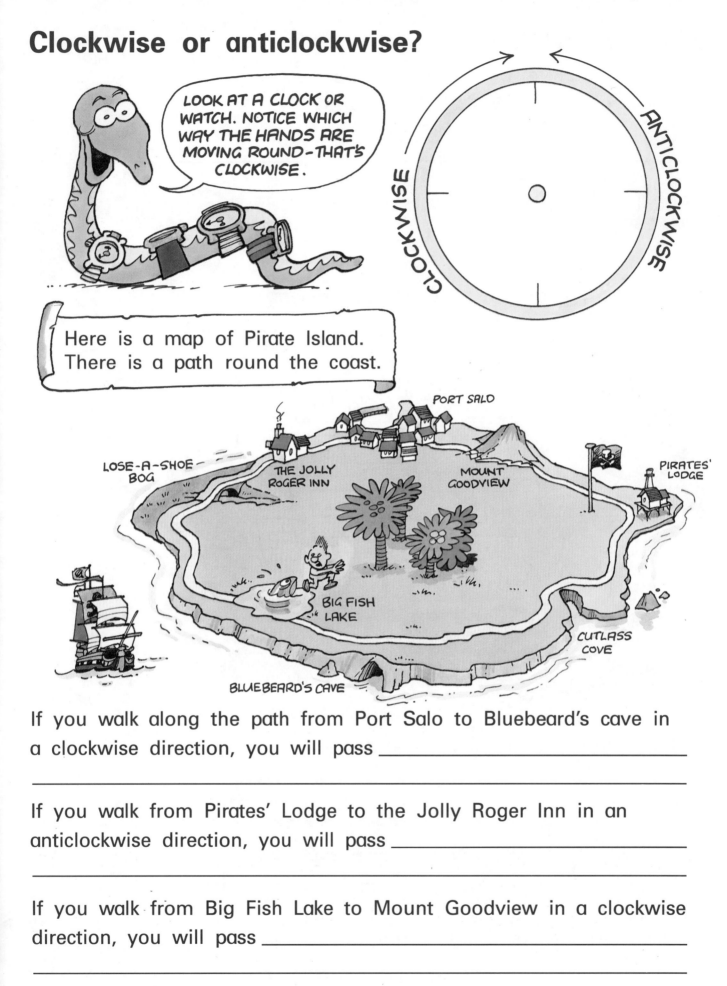

LOOK AT A CLOCK OR WATCH. NOTICE WHICH WAY THE HANDS ARE MOVING ROUND — THAT'S CLOCKWISE.

CLOCKWISE

ANTICLOCKWISE

Here is a map of Pirate Island. There is a path round the coast.

PORT SALO

LOSE-A-SHOE BOG

THE JOLLY ROGER INN

MOUNT GOODVIEW

PIRATES' LODGE

BIG FISH LAKE

CUTLASS COVE

BLUEBEARD'S CAVE

If you walk along the path from Port Salo to Bluebeard's cave in a clockwise direction, you will pass _____

_____

If you walk from Pirates' Lodge to the Jolly Roger Inn in an anticlockwise direction, you will pass _____

_____

If you walk from Big Fish Lake to Mount Goodview in a clockwise direction, you will pass _____

_____

Compass points

Here are the points of the compass:

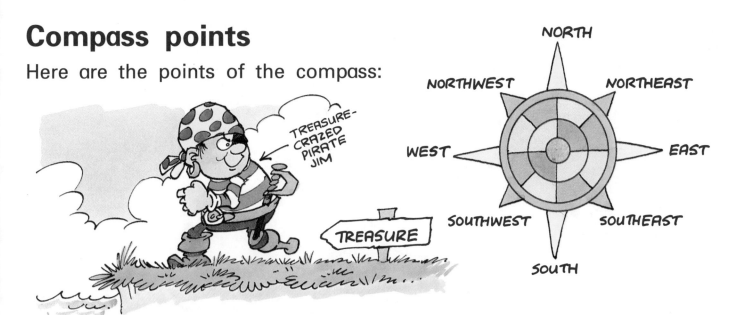

If Port Salo is the place furthest north on the island, what is the place furthest south? _____

What would you find in the northwest corner of the island?

_____

If you walked from Mount Goodview to Big Fish Lake through the jungle, in which direction would you be walking?

_____

Buried treasure!

Follow the directions below. They should lead you to buried treasure. Draw your route on the map of Pirate Island and put an **X** where the treasure is.

> START AT PORT SALO.
>
> GO <u>WEST</u> FOR A BOTTLE OF GROG AND A BITE TO EAT.
> THEN HEAD <u>SOUTHWEST</u> OVER THE BRIDGE. DON'T GET YOUR FEET WET!
> NOW GO <u>EAST</u> THROUGH THE JUNGLE. STOP AND HEAD <u>NORTH</u> TO ADMIRE THE VIEW.
> GO <u>SOUTHEAST</u> AND RAISE THE FLAG.
> DUE <u>SOUTH</u> AS FAR AS YOU CAN GO SHOULD BRING YOU TO THE TREASURE!

Hundreds, tens and units

Look at this number.

THIS TELLS YOU HOW MANY HUNDREDS THERE ARE.

4 2 6

THIS TELLS YOU HOW MANY TENS THERE ARE.

THIS TELLS YOU HOW MANY UNITS THERE ARE.

CLEVER DOG THAT!

426 can be shown on an abacus like this:

THERE ARE 4 HUNDREDS 2 TENS AND 6 UNITS.

4 2 6
H T U

Which numbers are shown here?

H T U   H T U   H T U   H T U

Draw beads on the abacuses to show these numbers:

| 3 | 6 | 4 | | 2 | 5 | 9 | | 6 | 3 | 1 | | 7 | 0 | 4 |
| H | T | U | | H | T | U | | H | T | U | | H | T | U |

Now put all the numbers in order, starting with the smallest.

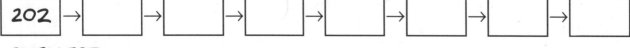

202 → ☐ → ☐ → ☐ → ☐ → ☐ → ☐ → ☐

SMALLEST

Place value

Each of these shapes contains three digits.

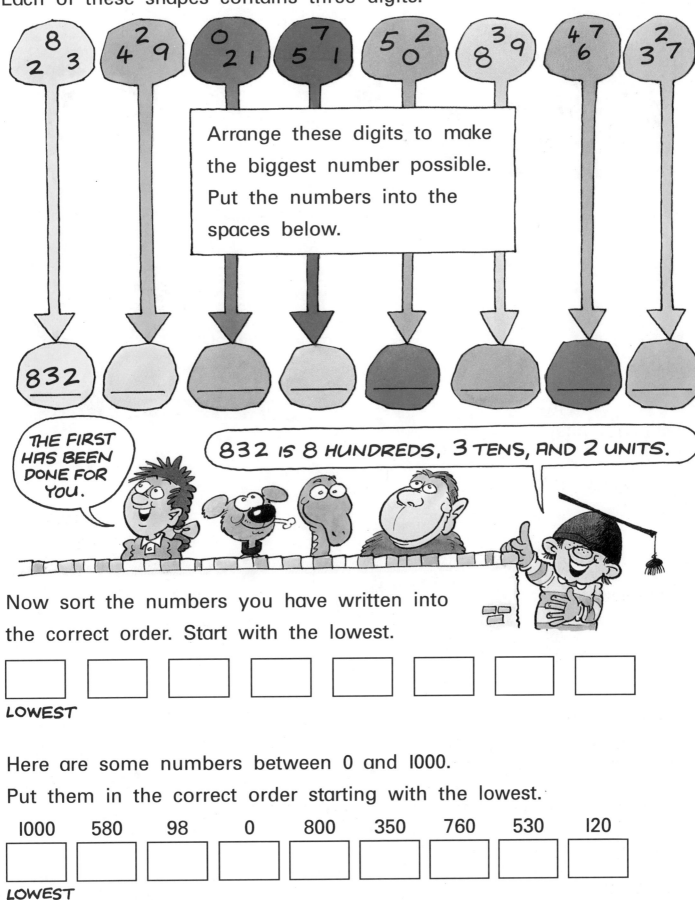

Arrange these digits to make the biggest number possible. Put the numbers into the spaces below.

832

THE FIRST HAS BEEN DONE FOR YOU.

832 IS 8 HUNDREDS, 3 TENS, AND 2 UNITS.

Now sort the numbers you have written into the correct order. Start with the lowest.

LOWEST

Here are some numbers between 0 and 1000.

Put them in the correct order starting with the lowest.

1000	580	98	0	800	350	760	530	120

LOWEST

Vertical addition

Sixteen bees add three more bees is nineteen bees.

This can be written as a sum:

16 + 3 = 19 or like this:

```
  16
+  3
————
  19
```

6 UNITS + 3 UNITS IS 9 UNITS AND 1 TEN EQUALS 19.

ALWAYS ADD THE NUMBERS IN THE UNITS COLUMN FIRST.

BIGGER SUMS ARE EASIER IF WRITTEN VERTICALLY.

Can you add these?
Write your answers in the boxes.

Ten mice add four mice

```
  10
+  4
————
```

Twelve cakes add six more cakes

```
  12
+  6
————
```

YUM YUM!

Now try these.

EASY NUMBERS

$$\begin{array}{r} 7 \\ +\ 2 \\ \hline \end{array}$$ $$\begin{array}{r} 5 \\ +\ 4 \\ \hline \end{array}$$ $$\begin{array}{r} 6 \\ +\ 3 \\ \hline \end{array}$$ $$\begin{array}{r} 4 \\ +\ 4 \\ \hline \end{array}$$ $$\begin{array}{r} 2 \\ +\ 3 \\ \hline \end{array}$$ $$\begin{array}{r} 4 \\ +\ 1 \\ \hline \end{array}$$

BIGGER NUMBERS

$$\begin{array}{r} 17 \\ +\ 2 \\ \hline \end{array}$$ $$\begin{array}{r} 15 \\ +\ 2 \\ \hline \end{array}$$ $$\begin{array}{r} 16 \\ +\ 3 \\ \hline \end{array}$$ $$\begin{array}{r} 24 \\ +\ 4 \\ \hline \end{array}$$ $$\begin{array}{r} 12 \\ +\ 3 \\ \hline \end{array}$$ $$\begin{array}{r} 4 \\ +\ 21 \\ \hline \end{array}$$

THREE NUMBERS

$$\begin{array}{r} 8 \\ +\ 6 \\ 9 \\ \hline \end{array}$$ $$\begin{array}{r} 7 \\ +\ 7 \\ 2 \\ \hline \end{array}$$ $$\begin{array}{r} 8 \\ +\ 9 \\ 9 \\ \hline \end{array}$$ $$\begin{array}{r} 6 \\ +10 \\ 3 \\ \hline \end{array}$$ $$\begin{array}{r} 7 \\ +\ 3 \\ 9 \\ \hline \end{array}$$ $$\begin{array}{r} 21 \\ +\ 1 \\ 11 \\ \hline \end{array}$$

ENORMOUS NUMBERS

$$\begin{array}{r} 52 \\ +23 \\ \hline \end{array}$$ $$\begin{array}{r} 16 \\ +71 \\ \hline \end{array}$$ $$\begin{array}{r} 28 \\ +10 \\ \hline \end{array}$$ $$\begin{array}{r} 27 \\ +12 \\ \hline \end{array}$$ $$\begin{array}{r} 43 \\ +26 \\ \hline \end{array}$$ $$\begin{array}{r} 54 \\ +45 \\ \hline \end{array}$$

Which egg belongs to which hen?
Draw a line from each egg to the correct hen.

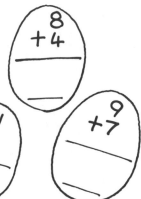

Who has laid the most eggs? ☐

13

Vertical subtraction

When we take away (subtract), we use the – sign.

Here are fifteen apples.
The farmer's wife takes away four apples.

There are eleven apples left.

We can write this as a sum:

15 – 4 = 11   or vertically like this: _15
                                            4
                                           ‾‾‾
                                            11

BEGIN WITH THE UNITS.

ALWAYS SUBTRACT THE NUMBERS ON THE RIGHT FIRST.

I'VE DONE THE FIRST TWO FOR YOU!

NOW TRY THESE.

_18 5 ‾‾‾ 13	_23 2 ‾‾‾ 21	_17 5 ‾‾‾	_28 6 ‾‾‾	_27 3 ‾‾‾	_53 12 ‾‾‾
_65 23 ‾‾‾	_82 41 ‾‾‾	_70 50 ‾‾‾	_59 37 ‾‾‾	_97 45 ‾‾‾	_56 20 ‾‾‾
_72 62 ‾‾‾	_83 22 ‾‾‾	_98 38 ‾‾‾	_67 17 ‾‾‾	_84 14 ‾‾‾	_28 14 ‾‾‾

Odd or even?

Who is Ben going to meet?
Fill in the answers to find out.
If the answer is an **odd** number, follow ODD ⇨
If the answer is an **even** number, follow EVEN ⇨

ODD NUMBERS ALWAYS END IN 1 3 5 7 OR 9.

EVEN NUMBERS ALWAYS END IN 0 2 4 6 OR 8.

LOOK CAREFULLY AT EACH SUM. IS THE SYMBOL + OR − ?

START

4 + 6 = ☐   ODD →←EVEN   3 − 2 = ☐

6 + 6 = ☐   7 + 4 = ☐

13 − 5 = ☐   17 − 5 = ☐

4 + 4 = ☐

10 + 9 = ☐   11 + 2 = ☐

3 + 3 = ☐

15

Coded messages

Here is the start of a simple code.

A	B	C	D	E	F	G	H	I	J	K	L	M
1	2	3	4	5								

N	O	P	Q	R	S	T	U	V	W	X	Y	Z
	15					21						26

Can you see the number pattern?
Put in the missing numbers.

Now decode this message.

| 23 | 8 | 1 | 20 |

| 4 | 15 |

| 25 | 15 | 21 |

| 7 | 9 | 22 | 5 |

| 1 | 14 |

| 5 | 12 | 5 | 16 | 8 | 1 | 14 | 20 |

| 23 | 9 | 20 | 8 |

| 2 | 9 | 7 |

| 6 | 5 | 5 | 20 |

| 16 | 12 | 5 | 14 | 20 | 25 |

| 15 | 6 |

| 18 | 15 | 15 | 13 |

16

Here is a new code.

A	B	C	D	E	F	G	H	I	J	K	L	M
0	3	6	9	12	15	18	21	24	27	30	33	36

N	O	P	Q	R	S	T	U	V	W	X	Y	Z
39	42	45	48	51	54	57	60	63	66	69	72	75

CAN YOU SEE THE NUMBER PATTERN?

Answer the sums. Then use the code to find the letter that goes with each answer.
What is the message?

```
 +45    +17    -48    + 3    -28
  21      4     24      3      7
 ----   ----   ----   ----   ----

 ....   ....   ....   ....   ....
```

```
 +21    -24    -55    +54    +12    +11    -28          +20    +50
  30     12     10      3     12     22     16            4      4
 ----   ----   ----   ----   ----   ----   ----         ----   ----

 ....   ....   ....   ....   ....   ....   ....         ....   ....
```

```
 + 9    -54    +30    + 4          - 6    +50          +30    + 0    +53    -22    +52
   9     12     12      5            6      7            6      0      4      1      2
 ----   ----   ----   ----         ----   ----         ----   ----   ----   ----   ----
                                                                                    ?
 ....   ....   ....   ....         ....   ....         ....   ....   ....   ....   ....
```

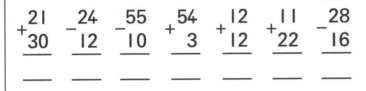

```
 - 4    +30          -14    + 6    + 3    + 4    -61
   4      9           14      3      6      8     10
 ----   ----         ----   ----   ----   ----   ----
                                                   !
 ....   ....         ....   ....   ....   ....   ....
```

I'M A PYTHON!

Drawing numbers

You can draw numbers on squared paper by counting the little squares.
Here are three ways that 20 can be drawn:

REMEMBER, COLUMNS GO UP AND DOWN, ROWS GO ACROSS!

like this 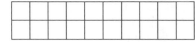 I row of 20 squares

like this 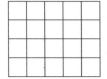 2 rows of 10 squares

or like this  4 rows of 5 squares

I row of 20 squares can be written as a multiplication sum, like this:

$$1 \times 20 = 20$$

2 rows of 10 squares → $2 \times 10 = 20$

4 rows of 5 squares → $4 \times 5 = 20$

Try drawing these numbers at least two different ways.

WRITE THE MULTIPLICATION SUM NEXT TO EACH DRAWING.

16

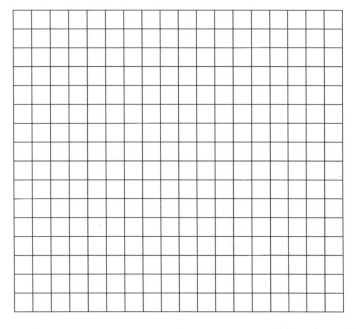

24

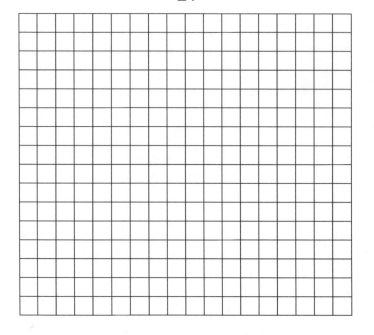

How many ways can you draw 40?

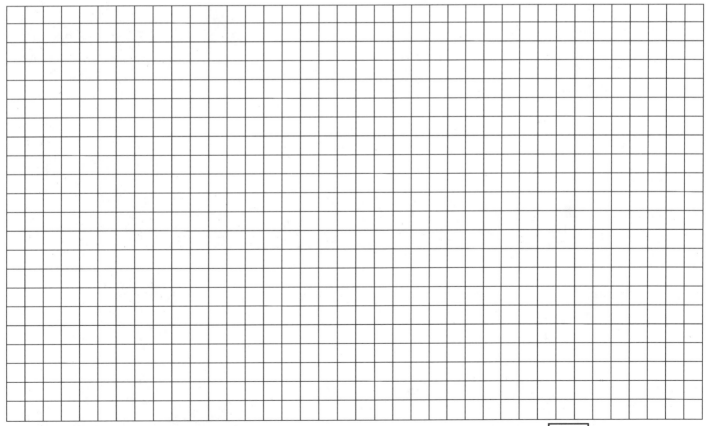

…UMM.

Now try some odd numbers, like 17 or 21.
Watch out – odd numbers are more difficult!

How many sums have you done on these two pages?

Sharing equally

÷ IS THE SIGN FOR SHARING OR DIVIDING.

Here are 12 buns. If they were shared equally among 3 elephants, how many would each elephant get?

Each elephant would get 4 buns.
12 buns shared among 3 elephants = 4 buns each.

This can be written as a division sum:

$12 ÷ 3 = 4$

Share these nuts equally between two squirrels.
How many nuts will each squirrel get?

$16 ÷ 2 = \boxed{}$

Share these eggs equally among three nests.
How many eggs in each nest?

$18 ÷ 3 = \boxed{}$

Divide these carrots equally among five rabbits.
How many carrots will each rabbit get?

$15 ÷ 5 = \boxed{}$

Divide these flowers equally between two tubs.
How many flowers in each tub?

$14 ÷ 2 = \boxed{}$

Dividing with remainders

Try to divide seven objects such as biscuits, buttons or pencils equally among three plates.

We can say: seven divided by three is two remainder one.
This can be written as a sum:

7 ÷ 3 = 2 remainder 1

Now try these.

> THE AMOUNT LEFT OVER IS CALLED THE REMAINDER.

> USE REAL OBJECTS SUCH AS COUNTERS OR BUTTONS TO HELP YOU.

13 ÷ 3 = [4] rem [1]

15 ÷ 4 = [ ] rem [ ]

18 ÷ 7 = [ ] rem [ ]

25 ÷ 6 = [ ] rem [ ]

17 ÷ 5 = [ ] rem [ ]

11 ÷ 2 = [ ] rem [ ]

24 ÷ 5 = [ ] rem [ ]

17 ÷ 8 = [ ] rem [ ]

10 ÷ 3 = [ ] rem [ ]

23 ÷ 4 = [ ] rem [ ]

9 ÷ 2 = [ ] rem [ ]

10 ÷ 9 = [ ] rem [ ]

> REM IS SHORT FOR REMAINDER.

REM

How could 4 sausages be divided equally among 3 boys without a remainder?

Multiplication squares

Here is a multiplication square.
To fill in the gaps, multiply the number across the bottom by the number down the side.

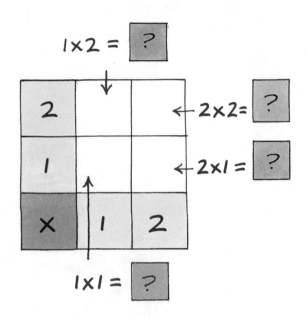

I'VE FILLED IN EACH *GAP* WITH THE ANSWER.

Now complete this multiplication square.

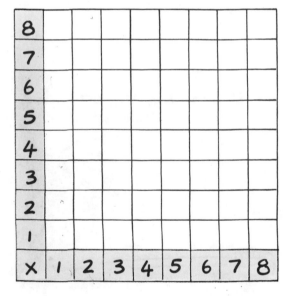

LOOK FOR THE PATTERNS.

Use your multiplication square to answer these sums:

$4 \times 3 =$ ☐ $6 \times 4 =$ ☐ $5 \times 4 =$ ☐

$2 \times 5 =$ ☐ $6 \times 5 =$ ☐ $1 \times 6 =$ ☐

$5 \times 3 =$ ☐ $3 \times 5 =$ ☐ $4 \times 4 =$ ☐

22

Going shopping

Look at the shop.

What is the cheapest item on sale?_____

What is the most expensive item?_____

Robert has been given these coins:

How much money does he have altogether? ▢

How much money will he need to
buy everything on his shopping list? ▢

SHOPPING LIST

1 comic
3 pens
2 paintbrushes
4 apples
2 note pads
6 lollipops

How much money will Robert have left? ▢

Guesswork

Estimate the length of this line.

I estimate that it is ☐ cm long.

Now measure the line.
The line measures ☐ cm.

ESTIMATE MEANS GUESS.

IF YOU GUESSED WITHIN 2 CM - THAT'S A GOOD ESTIMATE!

Estimate the length or height of the objects below.
Don't measure until each estimate has been written!

Object	Estimate	Actual Measurement	Tick if a good estimate
length of this book	cm	cm	within 3cm
width of this book when open	cm	cm	within 5cm
distance round your head	cm	cm	within 15cm
distance across the top of a cup	cm	cm	within 3cm
height of a window	cm	cm	within 30cm
height of a chair	cm	cm	within 20cm
distance round an apple	cm	cm	within 15cm
the diagonal distance across a table	cm	cm	within 20cm

Think of two more of your own
